094515

ECDL® Advanced 2.0

Revision Series

Module AM3

Word Processing

using
Microsoft® Word

Release RS12v1

Revision Series

Published by:

CiA Training Ltd
Business & Innovation Centre
Sunderland Enterprise Park
Sunderland SR5 2TA
United Kingdom

Tel: +44 (0) 191 549 5002
Fax: +44 (0) 191 549 9005

E-mail: info@ciatraining.co.uk
Web: www.ciatraining.co.uk

ISBN 13: 978 1 86005 806 6

First published 2009

Copyright © 2009 CiA Training Ltd

European Computer Driving Licence, ECDL, International Computer Driving Licence, ICDL, e-Citizen and related logos are all registered Trade Marks of The European Computer Driving Licence Foundation Limited ("ECDL Foundation").

CiA Training Ltd is an entity independent of ECDL Foundation and is not associated with ECDL Foundation in any manner. This courseware may be used to assist candidates to prepare for the ECDL Foundation Certification Programme as titled on the courseware. Neither ECDL Foundation nor **CiA Training Ltd** warrants that the use of this courseware publication will ensure passing of the tests for that ECDL Foundation Certification Programme. This courseware publication has been independently reviewed and approved by ECDL Foundation as covering the learning objectives for the ECDL Foundation Certification Programme.

Confirmation of this approval can be obtained by reviewing the Partners Page in the About Us Section of the website www.ecdl.org

The material contained in this courseware publication has not been reviewed for technical accuracy and does not guarantee that candidates will pass the test for the ECDL Foundation Certification Programme. Any and all assessment items and/or performance-based exercises contained in this courseware relate solely to this publication and do not constitute or imply certification by ECDL Foundation in respect of the ECDL Foundation Certification Programme or any other ECDL Foundation test. Irrespective of how the material contained in this courseware is deployed, for example in a learning management system (LMS) or a customised interface, nothing should suggest to the candidate that this material constitutes certification or can lead to certification through any other process than official ECDL Foundation certification testing.

For details on sitting a test for an ECDL Foundation certification programme, please contact your country's designated National Licensee or visit the ECDL Foundation's website at www.ecdl.org.

Candidates using this courseware must be registered with the National Operator before undertaking a test for an ECDL Foundation Certification Programme. Without a valid registration, the test(s) cannot be undertaken and no certificate, nor any other form of recognition, can be given to a candidate. Registration should be undertaken with your country's designated National Licensee at an Approved Test Centre.

ECDL Foundation
Approved Courseware

CiA Training's **Revision Exercises** for **Advanced ECDL** contain a collection of revision exercises to provide support for students. They are designed to reinforce the understanding of the skills and techniques which have been developed whilst working through CiA Training's *AM3 - Word Processing* book.

This practice material, which has been approved by ECDL Foundation, includes exercise items intended to assist Candidates in their training for an ECDL Certification Programme. These exercises are not ECDL Foundation certification tests. For information about authorised Test Centres in different national territories, please refer to the ECDL Foundation website at www.ecdl.org

Advanced Word Processing - The revision exercises cover the following topics, grouped into sections:

- Working Efficiently
- Text Editing

- Paragraph Editing
- Document Setup

- Tables
- Referencing

- Collaborative Editing
- Document Security

- Master Documents and Templates
- Field Codes and Forms

- Mail Merge
- Linking and Embedding

- Macros

A minimum of two revision exercises is included for the majority of sections. There are also general exercises, which cover techniques from any section of this guide. Answers are provided at the end of the guide wherever appropriate.

The Revision Exercises are suitable for:

- Any individual wishing to practise advanced features of this application. The user completes the exercises as required. Knowledge of *Word* is assumed, gained for example from working through the corresponding *AM3 - Word Processing* book produced by **CiA**.

- Tutor led groups as reinforcement material. They can be used as and when necessary.

Downloading the Data Files

The data associated with these exercises must be downloaded from our website: *www.ciatraining.co.uk/data_files*. Follow the on screen instructions to download the data files.

By default, the data files will be downloaded to the **CIA DATA FILES\Advanced ECDL Revision\AM3** folder in either **My Documents** or **Documents** depending in your version of *Windows*.

The data required to complete the exercises is in the **Data** folder and worked solutions for every exercise can be found in the **Solutions** folder.

If you prefer, the data can be supplied on CD at an additional cost. Contact the Sales team at *info@ciatraining.co.uk.*

Aims and Objectives

To provide the knowledge and techniques necessary to be able to successfully tackle the features of an advanced word processing application. After completing the exercises the user will have experience in the following areas:

- Applying advanced text and paragraph editing
- Working with master documents and modifying templates
- Tracking changes and working with comments
- Working with sections and columns
- Creating tables of contents, indexes, captions, footnotes and endnotes
- Using field codes, forms and document protection
- Editing mail merge documents
- Linking and embedding data
- Working with Macros

Office Versions

These revision exercises were written without references to any specific office version. The data is, however, Office specific and the correct set of data should be downloaded to match your office version.

Requirements

These revision exercises were created for *Microsoft Word*. They assume that the computer is already switched on, that a printer and mouse are attached and that the necessary programs have been fully and correctly installed on your computer. However, in *Word,* some features are not installed initially and a prompt to insert the *Office* CD may appear when these features are accessed.

Revision Series

The following revision exercises are divided into sections, each targeted at specific elements of the Advanced ECDL syllabus. The individual sections are an exact match for the sections in the ECDL Advanced Training Guides from CiA Training, making the guides an ideal reference source for anyone working through these exercises.

Working Efficiently

This exercise includes topics taken from the following list: Creating bookmarks and hyperlinks, saving files in different formats for various purposes.

Exercise 1

1. Open the document **Topperville Hall**.

2. In paragraph one, select the text **...Elizabethan architecture** and create a hyperlink to the web page **www.elizabethan-era.org.uk/elizabethan-architecture.htm**.

3. There are plans to possibly extend the document for use on the Internet. Create bookmarks to each of the following headings: **The House**, **The Gardens**, **Pets' Corner**, **Gift Shop** and **Tea Room**, using suitable bookmark names.

4. If you wanted to create a detailed document with a separate "chapter" on each of the areas mentioned in step 3, which type of document would work well?

5. Just the text of this document, without formatting, is to be saved. Save it in the correct format with the name **Topperville Text**.

6. The document is now to be saved with the formatting. Save it in the appropriate format with the name **Topperville Formatted**.

7. Finally, the document is to be saved in a format so that it can be viewed on the Internet. Save it in the appropriate format with the name **Topperville Net**.

8. Test the hyperlink in paragraph one.

9. Close the browser.

10. Close any open documents.

Text Editing

These exercises include topics taken from the following list: Using **AutoCorrect** and **AutoFormat**, creating **AutoText**, using advanced **Find and Replace** options, using **Paste Special** options.

Exercise 2

1. Open the document **Chinese New Year**.

2. Use **Find and Replace** to locate any underlined text.

3. How many occurrences are there?

4. Use **Find and Replace** to change any text in bold to bold italic.

5. On page 2, change the text wrapping so that text is wrapped **square** to the right of the bamboo graphic.

6. Copy the whole document.

7. Start a new document and paste in the copied text, ensuring that the original formatting is <u>not</u> brought with it.

8. Which command did you use?

9. Undo the paste action.

10. Now paste the copied text ensuring it keeps the original formatting.

11. Close the new document <u>without</u> saving.

12. Clear all criteria from the **Find and Replace** dialog box (click **No Formatting**).

13. Save the document as **Chinese New Year2** and close it.

Exercise 3

1. Open the document **Topperville Hall**.

2. Use **AutoCorrect** to create an entry that will automatically replace the initials **JM** with **Jeremy Montague** as you type.

3. At the end of the document, type the following paragraph to test the automatic text:

   Plans for the Future

   JM plans to restore the west wing of the hall, which was partially destroyed by fire in 2008. Once complete, this area will house the family art collection and will be known as the JM Gallery.

4. Create an automatic text entry that inserts the phrase **For further information, contact** and name the entry **Info**.

5. Insert this automatic text at the end of each relevant paragraph shown below, followed by the names and telephone numbers indicated:

The House	**Clara McTavish +44(0)121 123456**
The Gardens	**Joseph Spade +44(0)121 123457**
Pets' Corner	**Bunny Tompkins +44(0)121 123458**
Gift Shop	**Sunita Singh +44(0)121 123459**
Tea Room	**Betty Scone +44(0)121 123455**

6. Delete the **AutoCorrect** entry for **JM** and the **AutoText** entry for **Info**.

7. Save the document as **Topperville Hall2** and close it.

8. Open the document **Marine Zoology**.

9. Apply **General Document** automatic formatting to this document.

10. Notice that the automatic formatting has not been applied to the **Diet** heading. You should always check documents carefully after using this feature. Use the format painter to copy the formatting of the previous heading to the unformatted one.

11. Save the document as **Marine Zoology2** and close it.

Paragraph Editing

These revision exercises include topics taken from the following list: setting paragraph pagination controls, creating and modifying styles, applying outline levels to styles, amending line spacing and creating multilevel lists.

Exercise 4

1. Open the document **Republic**.

2. Create the following styles:

   First Title   Times New Roman, 16pt, centred, space after 18pt, level 1.

   Next Title   Times New Roman, 12pt, bold, left aligned, space after 12pt, level 2.

   Mainbody   Garamond, 12pt, justified, Line spacing at least 6pt, space after 6pt, pagination option to keep lines together, body text level.

3. Activate the **Show/Hide** feature and delete any blank lines used to add space between paragraphs.

4. Apply the **First Title** style to the first line of text, **The End of the Roman Republic**.

5. Apply the **Next Title** style to the headings **Dictatorship**, **Power Struggle** and **Emperor**.

6. Apply the **Mainbody** style to the rest of the text.

7. Print the document.

8. Modify the **First Title** style to be dark blue.

9. In **Outline View**, display only levels 1 and 2 and print the document.

10. Use **Outline** controls to move **Emperor** heading to the top of the list of subheadings, then down one position.

11. Turn off the **Show/Hide** feature. Save the file as **Republic2** and close it.

Exercise 5

1. Open the document **Chinese New Year**.

2. Amend the **Body Text** style to have **1.5** line spacing.

3. Ensure a single line of text will never be left alone at the top or bottom of a page in the **Body Text** style.

4. Amend the spacing before and after the **Subtitle** style to **6pt** and **12pt** respectively.

5. Create a **character** style, the colour must be red; name the style **Redletter**.

6. Apply the **Redletter** style to the first letter of each word in each of the headings.

7. Save the document as **Chinese New Year3** and close it.

8. Open the document **Woodland Lodges**.

9. Change the three existing bulleted sections to outline numbered lists, i.e. **Physical Well Being** as **1** and the list as **1.1**, **1.2**, **1.3** and **1.4**; **Mental Attitude** as **2**, and so on (see the following diagram).

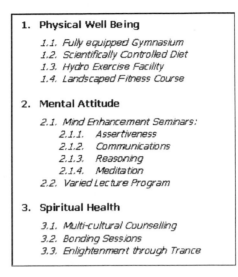

10. Save the document as **Woodland2**.

11. Close it.

Document Setup

These exercises include topics taken from the following list: adding and deleting section breaks, applying shading to parts of a document, creating multiple columns in a document, modifying column layout and width & spacing, section pagination and headers and footers and watermarks.

Exercise 6

1. Open the document **Topperville Hall**.

2. Insert continuous section breaks in the following locations:

   Before the first paragraph (not the heading) of **The Gardens** text.

   Before the heading of the **Pets' Corner** paragraph.

   Before the **Gift Shop** heading.

3. Apply 2 columns to the **Gardens** section.

4. Change the spacing between the columns to **0.7cm**. Balance the columns using a column break if necessary.

5. Force a new page before the **Pets' Corner** heading.

6. Apply 3 columns to the **Pets' Corner** text.

7. Change the column width to **5cm** and increase the spacing before the **Gift Shop** heading to **24pt**.

8. Insert a continuous section break before **The Gardens** title.

9. Apply landscape orientation to the **Gardens** section and change the top and bottom margins to **3cm**.

10. Change the page vertical alignment to **Center**.

11. Adjust any breaks (you can add or delete them) so that there are no spare pages, etc.

12. Remove the columns from the **Gardens** section.

13. Apply light grey shading to the **Gardens** and **Pets' Corner** sections.

14. Create a text watermark: **DO NOT COPY**.

15. Save the document as **Topperville Hall3** and close it.

Exercise 7

1. Open the document **Computer Info**.

2. Insert continuous section breaks in the following locations:

   a) Before the heading **About the Personal Computer**.

   b) Before the heading **About IT**.

   c) Before the heading **About Input and Output Devices**.

   d) Before the heading **About Storing Information**.

e) Before the second paragraph in **About Storing Information**.

f) Before the heading **About Files**.

g) Before the heading **About Networks**.

h) Before the heading **About the Internet….**

i) Before the heading **About Viruses**.

3. Apply 2 columns to the text (not the heading) referring to input and output devices.

4. Insert a page break before the **About Input and Output Devices** title.

5. In the paragraph **About Storing Information**, apply 2 columns to the section beneath the table.

6. Make sure a line separates these columns.

7. Change the spacing between columns to **0.5cm**.

8. Apply a setting to keep the **Intranets** heading and paragraph together.

9. Shade all of the text referring to viruses.

10. Apply headers and footers to the sections, with different odd and even pages. On odd pages, the header **Computer Formatting** must be at the left and the page number must be shown at the left of the footer. On even pages, the same header must appear at the right and page numbers at the right of the footer.

11. Save the document as **Computer Formatting** and close it.

Tables

These exercises include topics taken from the following list: merging and splitting cells, automatic table formatting, converting text to a table, sorting data, performing calculations.

Exercise 8

1. Start a new document and create a table to match the one below, to record attendance of a group of trainee soldiers on a variety of army assault courses.

Week Commencing:				
Soldier ID	Course 1	Course 2	Course 3	Course 4
		Number of successful completions:		

2. Apply automatic formatting using the **Table Colorful 1** style (use any **Style** in *2007*).

3. Save the document as **Squaddies** and close it.

4. Start another document and create the following table. Include the shading.

Regional warehouse location:			
Part No.	No. in Stock	Item value	Total
		Total Stock Value:	

5. Change the cell vertical alignment to **Center** for the **Total Stock Value** cell.

6. Enter 8 records to complete the table.

7. Use a calculation to sum the total stock value in the bottom right cell.

8. Print a copy of the table, then convert the entire table to text, using **Tabs** as the field separator.

9. Save the document as **Stock** and close it.

Exercise 9

1. Start a new document.

2. Enter the text shown below, separating each item by pressing **<Tab>**.

Surname	First Name	Department	Annual Salary
Johnson	Robert	Catering	11,500
Singh	Indira	Personnel	18,750
Abdul	Jenny	IT Support	25,179
Franks	Peter	Personnel	16,275
Butler	Jane	Training	19,100
Harrison	Susan	Catering	11,500
Roper	Billy	IT Support	24,500

3. Convert the text to a table, separating by tabs.

4. Format the top row of the table as bold and centre align all of the text.

5. Change the text direction of the top row to vertical, reading from bottom to top. Adjust the cell size accordingly.

6. Change the cell vertical alignment to **Center** and the cell margins to **0.1** all round for this row.

7. Sort the data in ascending alphabetical order by surname.

8. Add an extra row at the bottom of the table.

9. Merge cells 1 to 3 in this row and enter the text **Sum of Annual Salary**.

10. Right align the text in this cell and make it bold.

11. In the fourth cell on the bottom row, perform an automatic addition calculation to add up salaries paid for the year.

12. Increase the size of the table to about 100 rows, adding rows beneath the one for **Singh**.

13. Define the top row of the table as a header row, which will repeat at the top of each page.

14. Set the properties of the table so that non-header rows will <u>not</u> be allowed to break over page endings.

15. Save the document as **Salaries**.

16. Close the document.

Referencing

These exercises include topics taken from the following list: creating, modifying & deleting footnotes & endnotes, creating, formatting & updating a table of contents and table of figures, adding & deleting bookmarks, creating & deleting cross-references, adding captions, changing caption options, creating & editing indexes.

Exercise 10

1. Open the document **Computer Info**.

2. Amend the **Section** style to be outline level 1.

3. Change the headings that are bold (not the italic section headings) to **Heading 2** style.

4. Amend the **Heading 2** style paragraph spacing to **6pt** before and after.

5. Create a new page at the beginning of the document and insert a table of contents, **Simple** format, showing 2 levels: **Section** at level 1 and **Heading 2** at level 2.

6. Above the table of contents, type **Contents** and format the text as **Times New Roman 18pt** bold, centred.

7. Use **Mark All** to create index entries for occurrences of:

    PC, Laptop, PDA, network, mainframe, device, IT, CPU, storage, drive, file, directory, folder, Internet, intranet, extranet, e-mail, virus.

8. On page 13, mark the words **disinfect** and **quarantine** as subentries to the word **virus**.

9. At the end of the document, force a new page and type **Index**, same format as the **Contents** heading.

10. Create an index after this heading, using the **Simple** format.

11. Use a function key to refresh the table of contents, and remove index marks.

12. Your manager has asked you to give a short talk about networks, but you feel you need to brush up. Bookmark the following text:

About Networks heading	page 9
ISDN	page 10
PSTN	page 10
ADSL	page 10

13. Test the bookmarks.

14. Save the document as **Computer Info2** and close it.

Exercise 11

1. Open the document **Swimming**.

2. On page **3**, insert the following footnote after the word **timetable** in the Introduction: **see the table overleaf for more details**.

3. Convert all the footnotes to endnotes.

4. The second endnote is no longer appropriate. Delete it.

5. After the text **timetable** on page **3**, type **(see** and insert a cross-reference to the table (**Table 1**), which shows the pool activities. Complete the reference by closing the brackets.

6. Insert captions below each graphic on pages 1 to 5, with the following text (you will need to make the graphic on page **1** slightly smaller):

Page **1**	**Figure 1 Family friendly**
Page **3**	**Figure 2 Serious swimmers welcome**
Page **3**	**Figure 3 View from café**
Page **5**	**Figure 4 Swimming lessons**.

    Note: *The captions beneath the floating graphics on page 1 and 5 will be in text boxes. This is OK.*

7. Create a table of figures on page 2, beneath the table of contents (in *XP/2003* the floating graphics will not be included. Don't worry about this). Format appropriately.

8. Format the **Table** caption numbers to be **A**, **B** etc.

9. Save the document as **Swimming2** and close it.

Collaborative Editing

These exercises include topics taken from the following list: adding and removing comments, edit comments, tracking changes to a document, accepting or rejecting changes, comparing and merging documents.

Exercise 12

1. Open the document **Chinese New Year**.

2. After **...a different date each year...** in the first sentence, insert a comment which reads **January or February**.

3. Add the following comments to the table on page 1, next to the name of the animal:

Rat	generous, imaginative, charming, quick tempered

Ox	natural leader, methodical, dexterous
Tiger	adventurous, brave, charming, shows initiative, impulsive
Rabbit	pleasant, co-operative, affectionate, sentimental
Dragon	popular, vivacious, fun loving
Snake	thoughtful, romantic, wise, charming
Horse	very hardworking, independent, intelligent, friendly
Sheep	charming, artistic, elegant, a worrier
Monkey	popular, intelligent, successful
Rooster	hardworking, forthright, makes firm decisions
Dog	faithful, honest, a worrier
Boar	tolerant, honest, a good friend

4. Edit the comment about the tiger - replace **impulsive** with **a risk taker**.

5. Delete the comment in the first sentence.

6. Save the document as **New Year Comments**.

Exercise 13

1. Open the document **Wonders**.

2. Turn on tracking.

3. Increase the size of the main title to **20pt**.

4. In paragraph 3 on page 1, replace **mastabas** with **tombs known as mastabas**.

5. On the final paragraph on page 2, insert a new sentence after sentence 1: **It is also thought to have been used as target practice during World War II**.

6. Print the document showing the changes.

7. Move to the start of the document.

8. Work through the editing; accept the first change to the font size.

9. Accept the change to the sentence about mastabas.

10. Reject the change about target practice.

11. Save the document as **Wonders2** and close it.

12. Compare and merge **Wonders** and **Wonders2** to a new document and save it as **Wonders3**.

13. Close any open documents.

Document Security

These exercises include topics taken from the following list: password protecting a document, changing passwords, removing passwords.

Exercise 14

1. Open the document **Sunny**.

2. Change security settings so that a password (**openme**) is required to open the document.

3. Change settings to prevent unauthorised changes to the document, using the password **changeme**.

4. Save the document as **Secured** and then close it.

5. Reopen the document **Secured**, entering the correct passwords.

6. Which of the passwords will enable you to make editing changes?

7. Embolden the final sentence and save the changes to the document using the same name, i.e. **Secured**.

8. Close the document.

Exercise 15

1. Open the document **Nursery**. This document has the password **security** applied.

2. Change the password required to open the document to **safety**.

3. Save the document as **Nursery2** and close it.

4. Check the new password has taken effect by opening the document **Nursery2** again.

5. Change settings to protect the document for comments and save as **Nursery3**.

6. Remove all password protection from the document and save it using the same name.

7. Check that password protection has been successfully removed, then close the document.

Master Documents and Templates

These exercises include topics taken from the following list: creating a master document, creating a subdocument, adding or removing a subdocument and modifying a template.

Exercise 16

1. Create a new, master document with the title **Egyptian Odyssey Holidays** (**Heading 1** style).

2. Beneath the title, enter the following text in the **Normal** style: **Choose an Egyptian Odyssey holiday and you will be amazed at the excursions you can take. Read this document for some examples.**

3. Save the document as **Trips**.

4. Insert the following files as subdocuments, in the order shown, to compose elements of the master document:

    Pyramid_Sphinx

    Luxor

    Valleys

    Balloon Trip

    Nile Cruise

5. Switch to **Print Layout** view and remove any unnecessary section breaks so that there are no blank pages.

6. Switch to **Outline** view, and collapse the subdocuments.

7. Save the document (as **Trips**).

8. Close any open documents.

Exercise 17

1. Open the document **Excursions**. This is a completed master document.

2. The balloon trip is no longer offered by the holiday company. Remove it from the master document, but leave the master document open.

3. In place of the balloon trip, the company is now offering scuba diving. Start a new document and insert the text file **Scuba.txt**.

4. Format the title as **Forte 18pt** dark red centred, the subtitle as **Arial Black 12pt** dark red centred and the body text as **Arial 11pt**, black, justified.

5. Insert the graphic **scubadiving** and position it between the second and third paragraphs.

6. Centre the graphic and ensure there is a **12pt** space above and below it.

7. Save this new document as **Diving** and close it.

8. Insert **Diving** as a subdocument, after the **Valleys** subdocument.

9. Save the amended master document as **Trips2**.

10. Print out the section on diving only.

11. Close any open documents.

12. Open the <u>template</u> **Company Fax** from the data files.

13. Replace the globe watermark with the picture **grapes.gif** from the data files.

14. Resize the picture to about twice its original size.

15. Move the picture until it is at the left of the **Notes** area of the fax.

CC:	[Click here and type name]				
□ Urgent	□ For Review	□ Please Comment	□ Please Reply	□ Please Recycle

Notes: Enter covering text here.

16. The company has moved to larger premises, **Unit 9**. Make the change on the fax.

17. Change the font of the address text to italic, **11pt**.

18. Change the banner **facsimilie transmittal** to **FAX**.

19. Save the fax as a template, to the data files location, as **Company Fax2**.

20. Close the document.

Field Codes and Forms

These exercises include topics taken from the following list: inserting, deleting, editing and updating field codes, locking or unlocking a field, creating and editing a form, changing form field options, protecting and deleting form fields

Exercise 18

1. Open the document **Survey**.

2. Change the red bullets to black numbers and apply a tab at **12cm** to each numbered line. Make sure the numbers are sequential across all lists.

3. For questions **1**, **3**, **4**, **5**, **6**, **7** and **9**, add a field at the tab position, allowing the options **Yes** or **No**.

4. For question **2**, add a field with the available options **Yes**, **No, too warm**, **No, too cold**.

5. For question **8**, the options should be **Yes**, **No**, **Don't know**.

6. For the bulleted list, insert fields that allow text entry, at a **6cm** tab position.

7. Limit the number of characters allowed for a name to **30**, ensuring the name will always appear in title case.

8. Add help text to appear on the **Status Bar, No more than 30 characters allowed**.

9. Add a checkbox at the end of the form, after the word **box**.

10. Ensure the form layout can't be changed inadvertently.

11. Save the form as **Survey2** and close it.

Exercise 19

1. Open the document **Fieldcodes**.

2. In the header, insert a right aligned field code which will show the author's name.

3. Which key press would lock this field to prevent updates?

4. Amend the field in the footer to show only the file name.

5. Insert page breaks before **The Great Pyramid** and **Red Sea Diving** headings.

6. Update the page numbers in the table of contents.

7. Delete the field in the header.

8. Replace it with a code that will show the current date each time the document is opened.

9. Ensure all field codes are displayed.

10. Save the document as **Fieldcodes2** and close it.

Mail Merge

These exercises include topics taken from the following list: editing a mail merge data source, sorting a data source, using different data sources and using **Ask** and **If...then...else** fields.

Exercise 20

1. Open the document **Party**. This letter has been created to be used in a mail merge. Open the file **Members** as the data source.

2. View the **Recipients List** from the data source (**Members**), which is linked to the document. You <u>may</u> need to search in the data files for the data source.

3. Sort the data by surname in descending alphabetical order.

4. **Maddy Mustard** has cancelled her membership. Amend the records accordingly.

5. **The Barnacles** have moved to **7 Chapel Drive, Riverside, Noplace**. Make the necessary changes.

6. Print the merged records.

7. Complete the merge to a new document.

8. Save the merged file as **New Members**.

9. Use **Party** for the next steps. The club has various rooms that can be used for functions.

10. In the second paragraph, delete the text **Function Suite**. In place of the deleted text insert an **Ask** field.

11. In **Prompt**, type **Enter the location of the function**. The **Bookmark name** is **Function_Location**.

12. At the first prompt for the **Ask** field, enter **Function Suite**.

13. Insert a **Ref** field, choosing **Function_Location** as the bookmark.

14. Complete the merge and at the prompt enter **Sapphire Room**.

15. Save the merged file as **New Function** and close it.

16. Close any open documents <u>without</u> saving.

Exercise 21

1. Open the document **Exhibition**. If a prompt about **SQL** appears click **Yes**.

2. This document is linked to the data source **Teachers**. You <u>may</u> need to search in the data files for the data source if prompted. View the list of potential recipients.

3. Sort the data source alphabetically by school.

4. Which school is at the bottom of the list?

5. You have been supplied with the wrong list of teachers; it is a list of language teachers, not IT coordinators. Use the **IT_Teachers** data source instead.

6. Melanie has a new colleague, Alison, who is going to deal with entry passes for residents of **Noplace**. Melanie will issue passes for all other areas.

    a) In the final paragraph, delete **Melanie** and insert an **If...Then...Else** field.

    b) The **IF** field is **City** and must be equal to **Noplace**.

    c) If the city is **Noplace**, the text to insert is **Alison**; if not, the text to insert is **Melanie**.

7. Continue the merge process and preview the letters, checking that the **IF** field is working. How many letters mention Alison?

8. Save the merged file as **IT Exhibition**.

9. Close any other open documents <u>without</u> saving.

Linking and Embedding

These exercises include topics taken from the following list: linking data from various sources, embedding data, modifying embedded/linked data, updating and breaking links.

Exercise 22

1. Open the document **Shrubbies**.

2. On page 2, beneath the table, but above the heading **How to...** enter the heading **Shown as a chart**. Format this text the same as **Our Best Sellers** at the top of the page.

3. Centred beneath this heading, embed the chart from the **Sales Chart** tab of the *Excel* file **Plant Sales**. Make sure the correct tab is shown in *Excel* before importing.

4. Resize the chart to fit between the page margins.

5. From the document, change the colour of the data series for **Week 2** to bright pink.

6. Change the text on the horizontal axis to bold. Resize the legend if necessary, so all references can be seen.

7. Save the document as **Shrubbies Embedded** and close it.

Exercise 23

1. Open the document **Woodland Lodges**.

2. Beneath the sentence **Prices for the current year**, <u>link</u> the spreadsheet extract **Lodges** and do <u>not</u> display it as an icon.

3. Ensure there is adequate space around the linked data.

4. Save the file as **Woodland Lodges2** and close it.

5. The price for August breaks has risen to **360**. In *Excel*, amend the data in **Lodges**.

6. Save the spreadsheet and close *Excel*.

7. Open the document **Woodland Lodges2** and update the links.

8. Beneath the spreadsheet extract type in **See linked file for customer feedback**.

9. Create a link to the document **Comments** and display it as an icon.

10. Break the link to **Lodges** spreadsheet.

11. Save the document as **Woodland Lodges2**.

12. Close the document.

Macros

These exercises include topics taken from the following list: recording a macro, running a macro, assigning a button to a macro.

Exercise 24

1. Open the document **Balloon Macro** and create a blank line after the last paragraph.

2. Record a macro named **Table** within this document only that will insert a 3 x 4 table, with columns 3cm wide and rows 1cm high picture file **map_of_egypt** as a printed watermark.

3. Create a second macro named **Header** in this document only that will insert the current date as a field at the left of the header.

4. Save the amended document as **Balloon Macro2**.

5. Assign the **Table** macro to a button with a pencil or paint palette picture.

6. Save the amended document.

7. Use the toolbar button to run the **Table** macro, to insert another blank table into the document on a new page.

8. Delete the **Header** macro from the document.

9. Save the document with the same name and close all open documents.

Exercise 25

1. Open the document **Space Shuttle Intro**.

2. Create a macro, stored in this document only, called **Orientation**. The macro should change the page layout to **Landscape**, with the page vertical alignment as **Center** and change all margins to **2.5cm**.

3. Assign the macro to a button with the image of a book.

4. Ensure the document is in **Portrait** and all margins are set to **3cm** and then test the macro using the button.

5. Create a second macro named **Signoff**, within the current document, that will add your name and job title (you are a rocket scientist) on two lines at the end of the document, e.g.

   Bob Farina
   Rocket Scientist

6. Place the cursor at the end of the text and test the macro.

7. Delete the **Signoff** macro from **Space Shuttle Intro**.

8. Remove the **Book** icon from the toolbar.

9. Save the document as **Space Shuttle Intro2** and close the document.

The following revision exercises can involve processes from any part of the ECDL advanced syllabus.

Exercise 26

1. Open the document **Space Shuttle Intro**.

2. Attach a comment to **destroyed in an explosion during ascent in January 1986** in paragraph 2. The comment is to read **7 crew members were lost**.

3. Without moving it, format the space shuttle image at the bottom of page 1 so that the text wraps tightly around the left side of the image only.

4. Delete the extra paragraph mark left where the image was originally, ensuring the text remains justified.

5. Change the widow and orphan setting on the last paragraph on page 1, to ensure that the last line will never appear on its own at the top of a page.

6. Create a new style named **Body**, based on the **Normal** style. This style is **Arial 11pt**, **Justified**, with **12pt** space before and after the paragraph. Apply the **Body** style to all text with the exception of the first two lines (headings).

7. Insert a caption that reads **Image 1** beneath the orbiter flight configuration image.

8. On page 2, create a heading above the paragraph **NASA is prepared...**, which reads **Conclusion**. Format this heading as **Arial 12pt**, bold and change the font colour to a darker appropriate colour.

9. Add a bookmark called **summingup** to the **Conclusion** heading.

10. The names of the space shuttle orbiters are to be made bold and italic and have their colour changed to dark red. Create a macro named **orbiters**, in this document only, to perform these actions on any selected text.

11. Assign the macro to a button, with a suitable icon. Use the button to format the orbiters' names on page 1, paragraph 1 and 2, and on page 2, paragraph 3 (**Conclusion**).

12. Insert a right aligned field in the header to show the file name. In the centre of the footer, insert a field to show the current date and time. Lock the field in the header.

13. Add a footnote to the text **orbit** in the second sentence. The footnote should read **The course around the earth followed by the shuttle**. Adjust the position of the lower image if necessary.

14. Convert the footnote to an endnote.

15. Apply a password to open the document (**space**) and a different password (**nasa**) to make any changes.

16. Save the file as **Space Shuttle2** and close it.

17. Open the document **Space Shuttle2** and type your name at the end of the text to ensure the passwords to open and modify have been applied.

18. Remove the **orbiter** button from the toolbar.

19. Save the changes to the document and close it.

Exercise 27

1. Open the document **Locations**.

2. Move and format the image so that the text wraps tightly to its left edge.

3. Edit the comment attached to the first bullet point to read **You should at least know the basics**.

4. Turn on tracking. Edit the footnote on page 1 by changing **edges** to **boundaries**.

5. Amend the **Paragraph Heading** style so that the associated text is always kept with the heading. Ensure this style is always followed by the **Text** style.

6. Amend the **Bullets** style so that the bullet colour is red.

7. In the **Costs** paragraph on page 2, change **when buying a property** to **when buying a property abroad**.

8. Insert a new paragraph heading at the end of the text with the text **Buyers on the increase**. Enter the associated text **The figures below show the steady rise in the number of owners of property abroad**.

9. Link the spreadsheet extract from the file **Graph** and centre it.

10. Save the file as **Locations2** and close it (the tracked changes are not accepted/rejected to ensure evidence of them remains).

11. Open the document **Property**. If a prompt about **SQL** appears, click **Yes**. This main document is attached to the data source **Buyers**. You <u>may</u> need to search in the data file location for it.

12. Sort the data source in alphabetical order by **Last Name** and then complete the merge, saving to a new file called **New Buyers**. Close the merged file and the **Property** file (<u>without</u> saving).

13. Copy the following styles from the **Locations** document to the document **Feedback** (if you know how to copy styles using the **Organizer**, then use this method; alternatively open **Locations**, make a note of the formatting of each of the styles, then set them up in **Feedback**): **Paragraph Heading**, **Bullets** and **Text**.

14. In **Feedback**, apply the **Paragraph Heading** style to the first line, **Home Seekers Abroad**. Apply the **Bullets** style to all of the questions and the **Text** style to the remaining text.

15. Add a further item - **Property magazine** - to the drop down list associated with **Where did you hear about the company?** Note that the field will not display the drop down list until the form is protected.

16. Add help text to this field, which will be available via the <**F1**> button. Enter the help text: **Leave blank if none apply**.

17. Add a tab at **10.5cm** to the bullets only. Insert a check box after the last word in the document, **box**.

18. Ensure the form data is protected and save as **Feedback2**. Close any open files.

Exercise 28

1. Open the document **Marine Zoology**.

2. Apply the **Heading 1** style to the **Introduction** heading and **Heading 2** style to the remaining headings, including the **Sharks** main heading.

3. Create a new style, **Main Body**, based on the **Normal** style, **Arial 11pt** justified, **6pt** after, body text level. Apply this style to the remaining text.

4. Promote the **Heading 2** headings to level 1 throughout the document.

5. Insert a table of contents before the **Introduction** heading, using the **Formal** format, showing 2 levels. Insert a page break after the table of contents.

6. Demote the headings that were promoted in step 4 back to level 2. Update the table of contents to show these changes.

7. Mark <u>all</u> occurrences of the names of shark species (**blue shark**, **great white shark**, **tiger shark**, **swellshark**, **Port Jackson shark**, **mako**, **Basking**, **whale**, **megamouth**, **lemon** and **grey nurse**) throughout the document as index entries. Do <u>not</u> mark the references to body form, i.e. **typical**, **mackerel**, **cat shark**.

8. Force a new page at the end of the document and type the heading **Index** formatted as **Heading 1**. Create an index on this new page, beneath the heading, using the **Formal** format. Update the table of contents so that the index is shown.

9. Format the index text in 2 columns. Ensure each column is **6cm** wide and that there is a line between the columns.

10. Create a watermark for the document using the file **sea.gif**. Ensure the image is not washed out and that its scale is **400%** (type in the value).

11. Ensure all entries in the table of contents and index are current.

12. Set up different odd and even headers and footers. On odd pages, the picture is to appear at the right of the header and page numbers at the right of the footer. On even pages, the picture is to appear at the left of the header and page numbers at the left of the footer.

13. Apply a security setting, so that the document may only be edited if a password is supplied. The password is **potter**.

14. Save the file as **Marine Zoology3**. Close the document and then reopen it to check the security setting is working. Close the document again.

Exercise 29

1. Open the document **Shrubbies**. This is a new staff newsletter for a garden centre.

2. Change settings so that whenever the letters **SGC** are typed, they are automatically replaced by **Shrubbies Garden Centre**.

3. At the end of the document, in the **Safety and Maintenance** section, add a final point on a new line: **SGC will not accept responsibility for accidents arising from disregard of these instructions**.

4. Create a new style, **Bulletpoints**, based on the **Text** style, but with a dark green bullet that looks like a flower or leaf. Apply this new style to the text in the **Safety and Maintenance** section.

5. Ensure **Our Best Sellers** is at the top of page 2.

6. In the sales table on page 1, merge the cells on the top row and centre the title. Insert a formula in the empty **Grand Total** cell, which will return the value of all sales, then format the table with a colourful style and centre it if necessary.

7. On page 2, beneath the spreadsheet extract, <u>embed</u> the chart **Shrubbies Sales**. Reduce the size of the chart so it fits neatly between the margins and ensure there is adequate space above and below it.

8. Change the chart area to pale green and the walls to mid green. All text on the chart must be **Comic Sans**, **9pt**. Ensure the legend text is visible.

9. Add the following comment to the chart: **OT: ornamental trees, CT: citrus trees, E: evergreens, FS: flowering shrubs, F: flowers, FT: fruit trees, IP: indoor plants**.

10. Add this comment to point 3 in the **Safety and Maintenance** section: **Do not place cacti or venus fly traps where small children may reach them**. Ensure all comments in this document are hidden.

11. Apply a setting so that a caption is automatically inserted below each new graphic, using the label **Image**.

12. On page 3, insert a suitable clip art image in the herb section, after the **Coriander** paragraph and before the **Oregano** paragraph. Ensure the image is in line with the text and centred. The image should be approximately **3cm** x **2½cm**. If you cannot find a clip, use **herb.gif** from the data files

13. Insert a page break before **How to...** on page 2.

14. Ensure the **Safety and Maintenance** section starts a new page 5. Insert a second suitable clip art image in this section, between the first and second bullet points, again ensuring the image is centred and in line with the text. If you cannot find a clip, use the image **tools.gif** from the data files.

15. The image should be approximately **4cm** x **2½cm**. Do not worry if the caption has moved away from the graphic, just select and centre it.

16. Add a field to the right of the header, to insert the current date in English format.

17. On page 1, above the **Plant of the Month** heading, insert a table of figures.

18. Change the layout of the picture of the orange tree so that the table at the bottom of the page is not pushed on to page 2 and ensure **Our Best Sellers** is at the top of page 2.

19. Apply a security setting, so that the newsletter may only be edited if a password is supplied. The password is **potter**.

20. Save the document as **Shrubbies2** and close it.

Exercise 30

1. Start a new, blank document, which is to act as a template for a customer questionnaire. The company offers several services and wants all of their questionnaires to have a corporate look.

2. Insert the image **sparkle.gif** into the header to create a logo. Do not use washout. Ensure the logo is no more than **1.5cm** high and move it to the centre of the header.

3. Set all page margins to **2.5cm**. Create the following styles:

> **Heading** Based on normal style, followed by **Maintext**, Arial 14pt bold, left aligned, 6pt before, 12pt after
>
> **Maintext** Based on normal style, Arial, 11pt, justified, 6pt after
>
> **Bullets** Based on **Maintext**, bulleted with the ➢ symbol.

4. At the top of the page, select the **Heading** style and type **Heading goes here**. Beneath this type **This is the style for the main body text** (if you have set the styles up correctly this should already be formatted). On the next line type **Bulleted text uses the Bullets style**. Apply the appropriate style.

5. Modify the **Heading** style to be centred. Save the document as a template in the **Templates** folder with the name **Corporate1** and close it.

6. Start a new document, based on the **Corporate1** template and create the questionnaire shown below. The first three questions use **Yes/No** drop down lists, the fourth uses a text field and the fifth uses a **Yes/No/Don't know** drop down list. The remaining fields are text fields.

7. For the first text field, add help text to appear on the **Status Bar**: **Please keep comments brief**. The **Telephone** and **e-mail** fields must be restricted to **30** characters.

Customer Satisfaction Questionnaire - Sparkle Cleaning Services

You have recently used Sparkle Cleaning Services for the first time.

As a valued new customer, we would appreciate you taking the time to answer the following questions:

> Did your cleaner arrive on time?   Yes
> Did they spend the agreed amount of time at your premises?   Yes
> Were you satisfied with the standard of cleaning?   Yes
> If not, why not?
> Will you be using the service again?   Yes

For our records, please supply the following information:

Name:

Company:

Telephone:

e-mail:

Thank you for taking the time to complete the questionnaire. Please return it in the enclosed prepaid envelope.

---

8. Add a footnote to the second question about the amount of time spent: **The agreed time can be found on your contract.**

9. Protect the form so only comments can be made. Change this setting so that only filling in forms is allowed. Save the file as **Sparkle**.

10. Open the document **Response**. This is a completed questionnaire returned by a customer.

11. Add a comment to the third response: **interview the cleaner about these comments**.

12. Save the document as **Response2** and close it.

13. Delete the **Corporate1** template.

Exercise 31

1. Open the document **Locations**. Amend the styles as follows: **Text** - **Verdana 11pt**, **Bullets** - **Verdana 11pt** italic, **Paragraph Heading** - **Verdana 12pt** bold.

2. Ensure the **Professional Help** heading is kept with the associated text.

3. Apply 2 columns to the **Costs** and **Making an offer** paragraphs and associated text.

4. Ensure the text **If you are not regularly living** starts at the top of column 2, using a column break.

5. Shade the columns with a 5% shade of grey.

6. Reduce the spacing between columns to **1cm**.

7. Use **Find and Replace** to locate all the column breaks in the document. What code is added to the **Find what** box?

8. Save the document as **Locations Edit** and close it.

9. Open the document **Feedback**. You have received instructions from head office to remove references to currently owning property abroad.

10. Delete the questions **Do you currently own property abroad?** and **If so, in which country?** and their associated form fields.

11. Protect the form, save it as **Feedback Edit** and close it.

12. A mailshot has previously been sent to new members of the property club **Home Seekers Abroad**. However, you have just been informed that the Smalltown letters have been blown away in a gale. Open the file **Property** (attached to the data source **Buyers**).

13. Filter the recipient list and create a mail merge which will only be sent to Smalltown residents.

14. Complete the merge and save the merge file as **Smalltown** and close all open files. Do <u>not</u> save the changes to **Property**.

15. Create a new master document. This is to act as a starting point for an information booklet, with sections for various locations. Using the **Heading 1** style, type **Information for Buyers**.

16. On the next line using the **Normal** style, type **Please refer to the relevant section for the country you are interested in**.

17. Beneath this, using the **Heading 2** style, type **France**. On the following line, in **Normal** style, type **Content about France here**. Select these two lines and create a subdocument from them.

18. Create further subdocuments, following the above pattern, for **Spain, USA, Australia and New Zealand**.

19. Save the completed master document as **Buyers Info** and close it.

This section contains answers to all specific questions posed in the preceding exercises, together with the name of the file or files containing the worked solution for each exercise.

Exercise 1

Step 4 A master document with the separate topics as subdocuments would work well for this purpose.

Sample solutions for this exercise are saved as **Topperville Text Solution**, **Topperville Formatted Solution** and **Topperville Net Solution** in the **Solutions** folder.

Exercise 2

Step 3 There are 5 occurrences.

Step 8 The command is **Paste Special**. Paste as unformatted text.

A sample solution for this exercise is saved as **Chinese New Year2 Solution** in the **Solutions** folder.

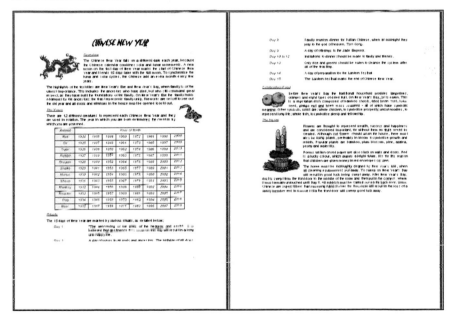

Exercise 3

Sample solutions for this exercise are saved as **Topperville Hall2 Solution** (not shown below) and **Marine Zoology2 Solution** in the **Solutions** folder.

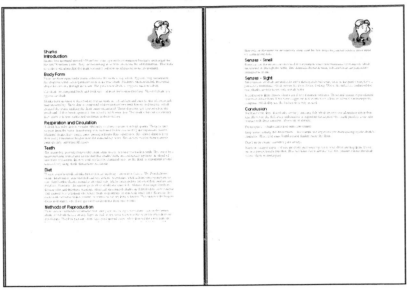

Exercise 4

A sample solution for this exercise is saved as **Republic Outline Solution** in the **Solutions** folder. You are required to obtain a printout showing the levels in the document, because when it is reopened (as in the solution file) they will not be on view.

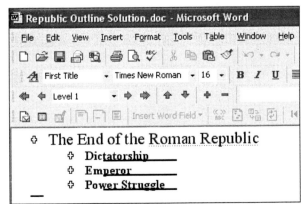

Exercise 5

Sample solutions for this exercise are saved as **Chinese New Year3 Solution** and **Woodland2 Solution** in the **Solutions** folder.

Woodland Lodges

At Woodland Lodges our concept is to expand and improve physical well being, mental attitude and spiritual health.

1. **Physical Well Being**

    1.1. *Fully equipped Gymnasium*
    1.2. *Scientifically Controlled Diet*
    1.3. *Hydro Exercise Facility*
    1.4. *Landscaped Fitness Course*

2. **Mental Attitude**

    2.1. *Mind Enhancement Seminars:*
        2.1.1. *Assertiveness*
        2.1.2. *Communications*
        2.1.3. *Reasoning*
        2.1.4. *Meditation*
    2.2. *Varied Lecture Program*

3. **Spiritual Health**

    3.1. *Multi-cultural Counselling*
    3.2. *Bonding Sessions*
    3.3. *Enlightenment through Trance*

We are open March to October. Prices for the current year are shown below:

Exercise 6

A sample solution for this exercise is saved as **Topperville Hall3 Solution** in the **Solutions** folder.

Exercise 7

A sample solution for this exercise is saved as **Computer Formatting Solution** in the **Solutions** folder.

Exercise 8

Sample solutions for this exercise are saved as **Squaddies Solution** and **Stock Solution** in the **Solutions** folder.

Exercise 9

A sample solution for this exercise is saved as **Salaries Solution** in the **Solutions** folder.

Exercise 10

A sample solution for this exercise is saved as **Computer Info2 Solution** in the **Solutions** folder.

Exercise 11

A sample solution for this exercise is saved as **Swimming2 Solution** in the **Solutions** folder.

Exercise 12

A sample solution for this exercise is saved as **New Year Comments Solution** in the **Solutions** folder.

the old year and all doors and windows in the house must be opened to let it out.

The Years

There are 12 different creatures to represent each Chinese New Year and they are used in rotation. The year in which you are born determines the creature by which you are governed.

Animal	Year of Birth								Comment
Rat	1924	1936	1948	1960	1972	1984	1996	2008	Comment [DH1]: generous, imaginative, charming, quick tempered
Ox	1925	1937	1949	1961	1973	1985	1997	2009	Comment [DH2]: natural leader, methodical, dexterous
Tiger	1926	1938	1950	1962	1974	1986	1998	2010	Comment [DH3]: adventurous, brave, charming, shows initiative, a risk taker
Rabbit	1927	1939	1951	1963	1975	1987	1999	2011	Comment [DH4]: pleasant, co-operative, affectionate, sentimental
Dragon	1928	1940	1952	1964	1976	1988	2000	2012	Comment [DH5]: popular, vivacious, fun loving
Snake	1929	1941	1953	1965	1977	1989	2001	2013	Comment [DH6]: thoughtful, romantic, wise, charming
Horse	1930	1942	1954	1966	1978	1990	2002	2014	Comment [DH7]: very hardworking, independent, intelligent, friendly
Sheep	1931	1943	1955	1967	1979	1991	2003	2015	Comment [DH8]: charming, artistic, elegant, a worrier
Monkey	1932	1944	1956	1968	1980	1992	2004	2016	Comment [DH9]: popular, intelligent, successful
Rooster	1933	1945	1957	1969	1981	1993	2005	2017	Comment [DH10]: hardworking, forthright, makes firm decisions
Dog	1934	1946	1958	1970	1982	1994	2006	2018	Comment [DH11]: faithful, honest, a worrier
Boar	1935	1947	1959	1971	1983	1995	2007	2019	Comment [DH12]: tolerant, honest, a good friend

Rituals

The 15 days of New Year are marked by various rituals, as detailed below:

Day 1   "The welcoming of the gods of the heavens and earth". It is believed that abstinence from meat on this day will result in a long and happy life.

Day 2   A day of prayer to all gods and ancestors. The birthday of all dogs, so they should be treated kindly and fed well.

Exercise 13

Sample solutions for this exercise are saved as **Wonders2 Solution** and **Wonders3 Solution** in the **Solutions** folder.

Exercise 14

Step 7 The password required to modify the document is **changeme**.

A sample solution for this exercise is saved as **Secured Solution** in the **Solutions** folder.

Exercise 15

A sample solutions for this exercise are saved as **Nursery2 Solution** and **Nursery3 Solution** in the **Solutions** folder.

Exercise 16

A sample solution for this exercise is saved as **Trips Solution** in the **Solutions** folder. Links to subdocuments will not be valid for the solution, as file locations will be different.

Exercise 17

Examples of the output from this exercise are saved as **Diving Solution**, **Trips2 Solution** and **Company Fax2 Solution** in the **Solutions** folder. Links to subdocuments will not be valid for the solution, as file locations will be different.

Exercise 18

A sample solution for this exercise is saved as **Survey2 Solution** in the **Solutions** folder.

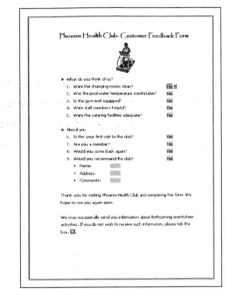

Exercise 19

A sample solution for this exercise is saved as **Fieldcodes2 Solution** in the **Solutions** folder.

Step 3   **<Ctrl F11>**.

Exercise 20

Sample solutions for this exercise are saved as **New Members Solution** and **New Function Solution** in the **Solutions** folder.

Exercise 21

Step 4   St Peter's Primary.

Step 7   There are 4 letters referring to Alison.

A sample solution for this exercise is saved as **IT Exhibition Solution** in the **Solutions** folder.

Exercise 22

A sample solution for this exercise is saved as **Shrubbies Embedded Solution** in the **Solutions** folder.

Exercise 23

A sample solution for this exercise is saved as **Woodland Lodges2 Solution** in the **Solutions** folder. You may have to edit the existing link so that it points to the location of the supplied solutions on your computer.

Woodland Lodges

At Woodland Lodges our concept is to expand and improve physical well being, mental attitude and spiritual health.

Physical Well Being
- *Fully equipped Gymnasium*
- *Scientifically Controlled Diet*
- *Hydro Exercise Facility*
- *Landscaped Fitness Course*

Mental Attitude
- *Mind Enhancement Seminars:*
  - *Assertiveness*
  - *Communications*
  - *Reasoning*
  - *Meditation*
- *Varied Lecture Program*

Spiritual Health
- *Multi-cultural Counselling*
- *Bonding Sessions*
- *Enlightenment through Trance*

We are open March to October. Prices for the current year are shown below:

Mar	Apr	May	Jun	Jul	Aug	Sep	Oct
195	230	250	280	320	360	280	230

Comments.doc

See linked file for customer feedback.

Exercise 24

Examples of the output from this exercise are saved as **Balloon Macro2 Solution** in the **Solutions** folder.

Exercise 25

A sample solution for this exercise is saved as **Space Shuttle Intro2 Solution** in the **Solutions** folder.

Exercise 26

A sample solution for this exercise is saved as **Space Shuttle2 Solution** in the **Solutions** folder.

Exercise 27

Sample solutions for this exercise are saved as **Locations2 Solution**, **New Buyers Solution** (not shown) and **Feedback2 Solution** in the **Solutions** folder.

Customer Satisfaction Questionnaire - Sparkle Cleaning Services

You have recently used Sparkle Cleaning Services for the first time.

As a valued new customer, we would appreciate you taking the time to answer the following questions:

➤ Did your cleaner arrive on time? No

➤ Did they spend the agreed amount of time at your premises? Yes

➤ Were you satisfied with the standard of cleaning? No

➤ If not, why not? He left dirty water in one of the sinks and the ladies' toilet was not cleaned thoroughly

Comment [DH1]: Interview the cleaner about these comments

➤ Will you be using the service again? Don't know

For our records, please supply the following information:

Name: Mona Lott

Company: Thickett and Pratt Solicitors

Telephone: 0123 456789

e-mail: mona_l@somewhere.net

Thank you for taking the time to complete the questionnaire. Please return it in the enclosed prepaid envelope.

Exercise 31

Sample solutions for this exercise are saved as **Locations Edit Solution**, **Feedback Edit Solution**, **Smalltown Solution** and **Buyers Info Solution** (**Smalltown Solution** and **Buyers Info Solution** not shown below) in the **Solutions** folder.

Step 7 The code for a column break is **^n**.

Home Seekers Abroad
To help us with market research, please take a few moments
to answer the following questions:
Where did you hear about the company?   Internet search
What type of property are you looking to buy?   House or villa
Do you want a property with a pool? Yes
Does the property have to be detached?   Yes
Are you looking near the coast or inland?   Inland
Do you want a rural or urban property?   Rural
Are you prepared to renovate?   Yes
Please supply your e-mail address
Thank you for taking the time to complete his questionnaire.
Please indicate if you would like us to e-mail you our monthly newsletter by checking the
box.

Other Products from CiA Training Ltd

CiA Training Ltd is a leading publishing company, which has consistently delivered the highest quality products since 1985. A wide range of flexible and easy to use self teach resources has been developed by CiA's experienced publishing team to aid the learning process. These include the following ECDL Foundation approved products at the time of publication.

- **ECDL/ICDL Syllabus 5.0**

- **ECDL/ICDL Advanced Syllabus 2.0**

- **ECDL/ICDL Revision Series**

- **ECDL/ICDL Advanced Syllabus 2.0 Revision Series**

- **e-Citizen**

Previous syllabus versions also available - contact us for further details.

We hope you have enjoyed using our materials and would love to hear your opinions about them. If you'd like to give us some feedback, please go to:

www.ciatraining.co.uk/feedback.php

and let us know what you think.

New products are constantly being developed. For up to the minute information on our products, to view our full range, to find out more, or to be added to our mailing list, visit:

www.ciatraining.co.uk